level 4

PIAN
SOLOS

by JANE SMISOR BASTIEN

KJOS WEST · Neil A. Kjos, Jr. Publisher · San Diego, California

PREFACE

The series, **PIANO SOLOS,** provides additional materials to reinforce concepts learned in **PIANO LESSONS.** However, the **PIANO SOLO** books may be used with any piano course for supplementary enrichment.

PIANO SOLOS primarily contains original pieces. In addition, some familiar songs and folk song arrangements are included.

The materials in this series are carefully graded for gradual progress.

SHEET MUSIC from **Level Four Solos** may be assigned to the student at the teacher's discretion.

At this point in the **BASTIEN PIANO LIBRARY,** the student has the background to go on to standard piano literature and supplementary materials in Levels 5 and 6 listed on the back cover.

ISBN 0-8497-5025-3

CONTENTS

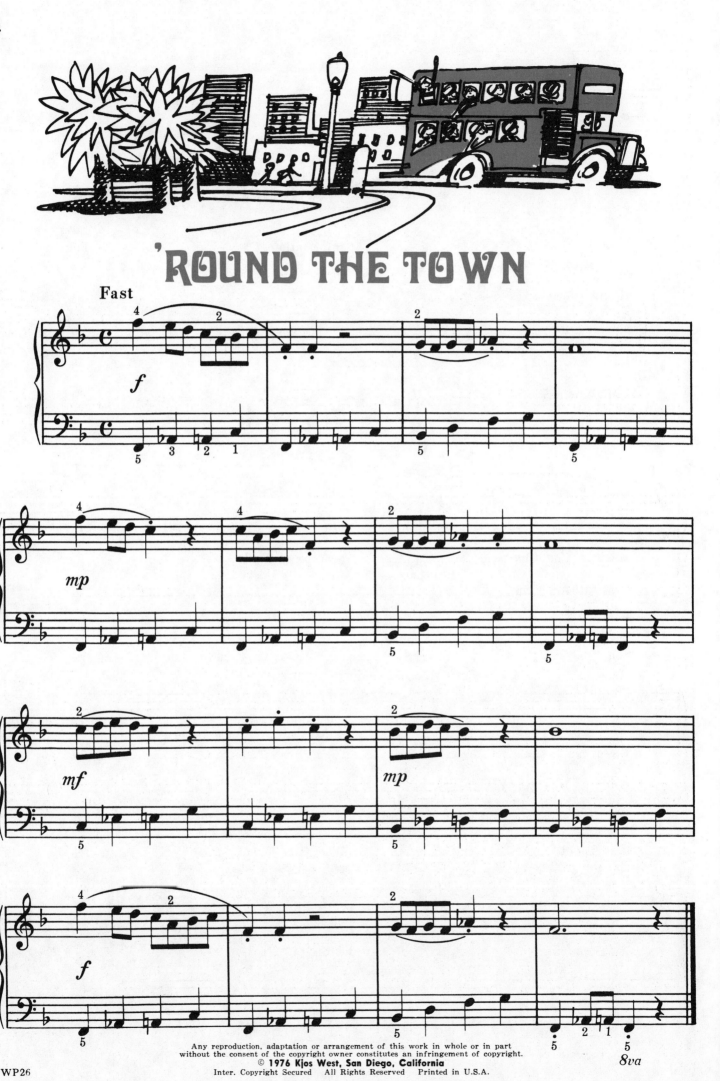

'ROUND THE TOWN

© 1976 Kjos West, San Diego, California
Inter. Copyright Secured   All Rights Reserved   Printed in U.S.A.

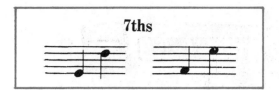

IN THE MOOD

"Overlapping" Pedal Sign

MORNING RIDE

GAVOTTE

WIND IN THE PINES

12

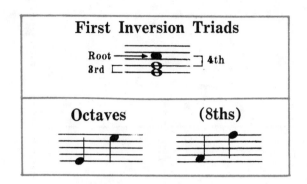

BELLS AT SUNDOWN

WP26

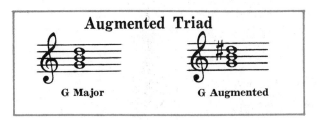

LITTLE DANCE

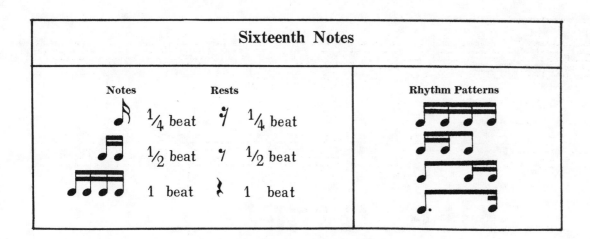

Sixteenth Notes		

ICE ~ SKATING

Smoothly

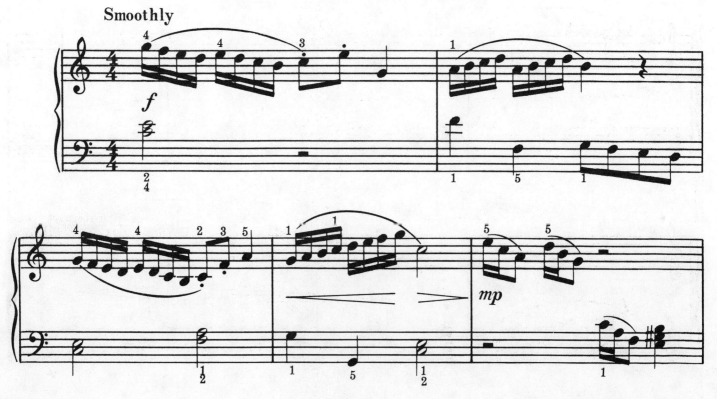

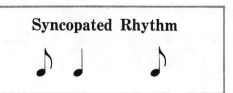

Syncopated Rhythm

MEXICAN CHA CHA

FESTIVAL AMERICANA

March tempo

TANGO TIME

SONATINA

With spirit

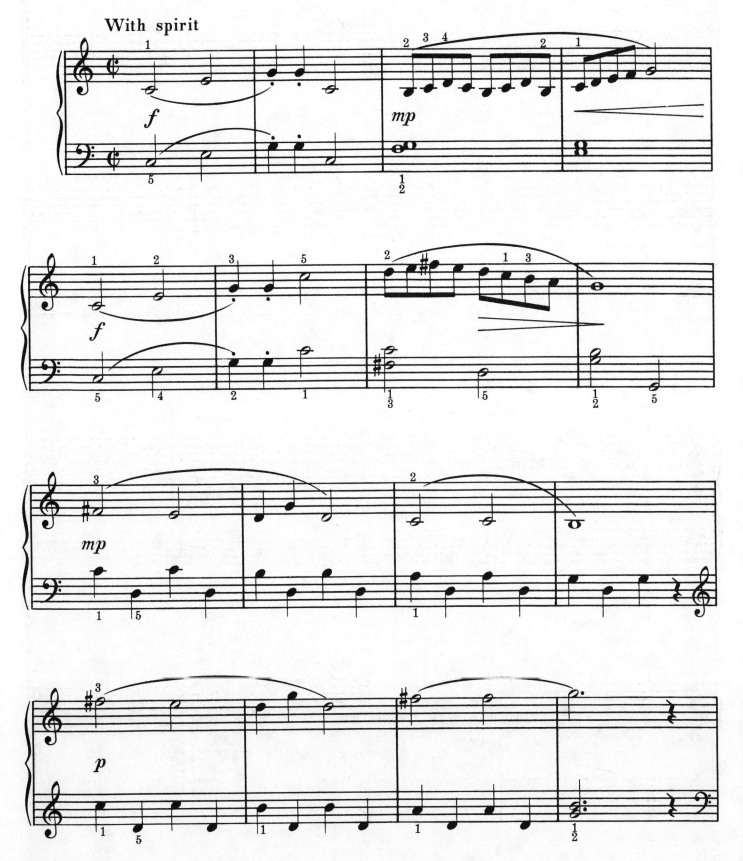

OCEAN PRELUDE

Maestoso

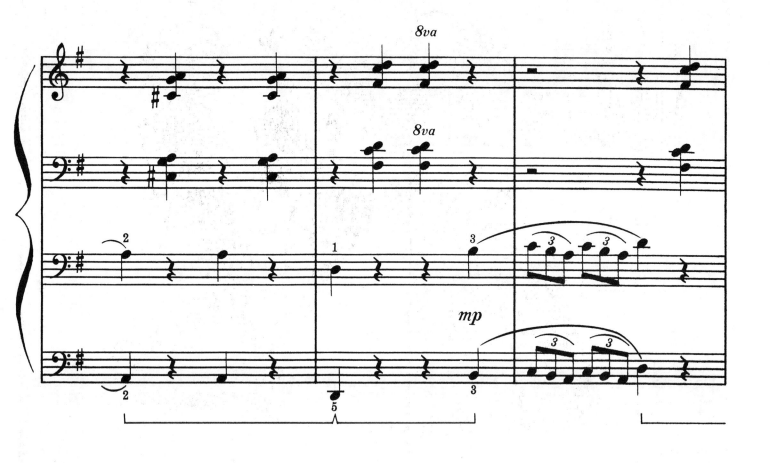

BAGATELLE

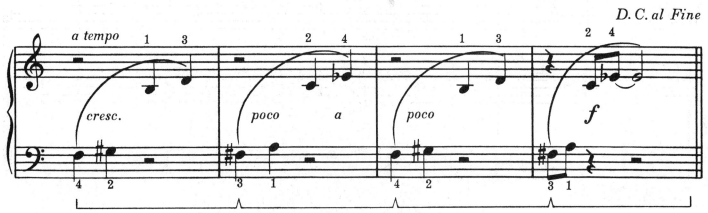

TOCCATINA

Allegro

WALTZ

THE STAR-SPANGLED BANNER

FRANCIS SCOTT KEY

JOHN STAFFORD SMITH

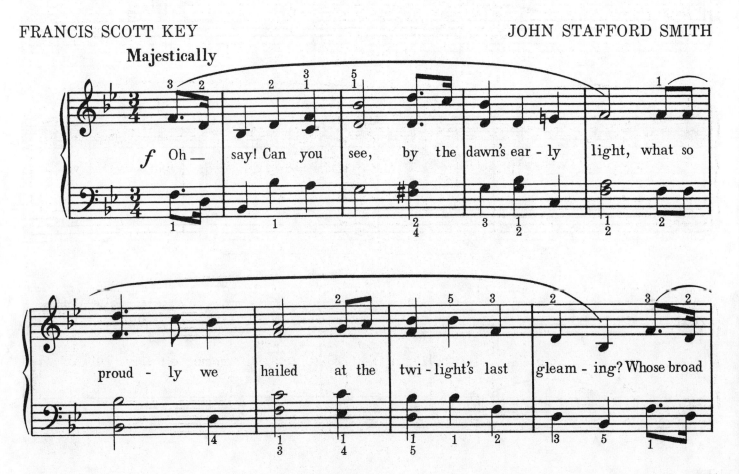

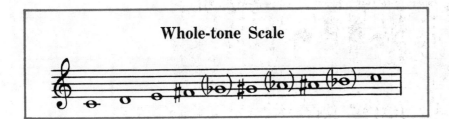

Whole-tone Scale

BLUE LIGHTS